First Edition, Revised August 2021.

Visit: www.whcornerstone.com/resources

ISBN: 978-1-63972-912-8

A WIDOW'S JOURNAL

A place to gather and reflect on your journey

PAULA HARRIS

This journal is dedicated to the loving memory of:

_____

Your spouse and partner died. You hurt. A lot.

You will heal. You will get back on your feet. You will Rise Up. You will navigate your path forward. It will take time. There will be lots of baby steps, mostly forward. But a few will be backward, so don't be surprised. Give yourself lots of grace.

Some days you will feel light, full of energy and able to tackle all that you need and want. However, some days you will want to pull the covers back over your head. And you will. And that's okay.

Your brain will likely be in a fog for a while. That is normal given what you are going through. This journal can be used to help you organize your thoughts and emotions as you work through your new reality.

Be kind to yourself. Don't hurry or rush. Your journey is personal. Your journey is not like anyone else's who has also been widowed, so don't compare.

Where to start:

- *Step one:* Review all the chapters so you get a sense of how the journal flows before jumping in.

- *Step two: Step two: Start at the beginning or jump in where you are most drawn to start. Choose the path that works best for you.*

- *Step three: There are no rules as to how you decide to use this journal. There is no time frame to complete it either.*

Please know that I will hold each recipient of this journal in light and prayer.

In love, peace, perseverance and hope.

Paula

Chapters

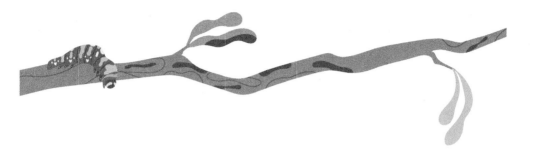

Chapter 1:
Suddenly Single

The reality has set in that your partner is not coming back and you are on your own. You know you need to figure out how you will navigate your path forward. Yet you don't know where to begin.

As you begin this chapter, consider these prompts to help you navigate your emotions as you reflect and journal.

- *Who do I need to reach out to for help or assistance?*

- *A comforting memory of my loved one is...*

- *What can I do at this moment to make the next few hours or days a bit better for myself?*

- *My hardest time of the day and/or week is...*

- *Who are the angels in my life who have appeared to support me and how?*

The following pages are filled with quotes to help prompt you to explore and capture other thoughts you might be having.

Never. We never lose our loved ones.
They accompany us; they don't disappear from our lives.
We are merely in different rooms.

—Paulo Coelho

If ever there is tomorrow when we're not together...there is something you must always remember. You are braver than you believe, stronger than you seem and smarter than you think. But the most important thing is, even if we're apart...I'll always be with you.

—A.A.Milne

We get no choice. If we love, we grieve.
—Thomas Lynch

Hope is important because it can make the present
moment less difficult to bear. If we believe that tomorrow
will be better, we can bear a hardship today.

—Thich Nhat Hanh

Never apologize for showing feeling.
When you do so, you apologize for the truth.
—Benjamin Disraeli

If the people we love are stolen from us,
the way to have them live on
is to never stop loving them.

—James O'Barr

Only a moment you stayed, but what an imprint your footprints have left on our hearts.

—Dorothy Ferguson

May the love of God heal you as the
burden in your heart abounds.

—Unknown

Tears are the silent language of grief.

—Voltaire

Weeping is perhaps the most human
and universal of all relief measures.
—Dr. Karl Menninger

The main thing in one's own private world is to try to laugh as much as you cry.
—Maya Angelou

Take sips of this pure wine being poured. Don't
mind that you've been given a dirty cup.

—Rumi

To fashion an inner story of our pain carries us into the heart of it, which is where rebirth inevitably occurs.

—Sue Monk Kidd

What we once enjoyed and deeply loved we can never
lose, for all that we love deeply becomes a part of us.

—Helen Keller

The song is ended,
but the melody lingers on.
—Irving Berlin

Life is a shipwreck, but we must
not forget to sing in the lifeboats.
—Voltaire

Real life isn't always going to be perfect or go our way, but the recurring acknowledgement of what is working in our lives can help us not only to survive but surmount our difficulties.

—Sara Ban Breathnach

He spoke well who said that graves are
the footprints of angels.
—Henry Wadsworth Longfellow

You don't get over it,
you just get through it.
You don't get by it,
because you can't get around it.
It doesn't get better,
it just gets different.
Every day, grief puts on a new face.

—Wendy Feireisen

He took half of my life with him when he
passed away. But he also left half of him
with me. I was still a whole person.

—Grace Liang, *Finding Grace:*

Chapter 2:
Grief Knows No Timeframe

You are wondering when this grief fog will pass and you will feel like your old self again. You ask others about their experience and you discover that everyone has a different answer. It might feel a bit unsettling that you can't predict how long this will last.

As you begin this chapter, consider these prompts to help you navigate your emotions as you reflect and journal.

- *Today, I'm having a hard time with...*

- *Am I comparing myself to other's journeys rather than just experiencing my own journey and is that serving me?*

- *I've been feeling a lot of...*

- *What is one thing that is preventing me from moving forward right now?*

- *What resources do I need to assist me through this grief?*

The following pages are filled with quotes to help prompt you to explore and capture other thoughts you might be having.

The reality is that you will grieve forever. You will not 'get over' the loss of a loved one; you will learn to live with it. You will heal and you will rebuild yourself around the loss you have suffered. You will be whole again but you will never be the same. Nor should you be the same nor would you want to.
—Elisabeth Kubler-Ross

Grief is the price we pay for love.
—Queen Elizabeth

Your present circumstances don't determine when you can go; they merely determine where you start.

—Nido Qubein

Rather light a candle than complain about darkness.
—Chinese proverb

Say not in grief 'he is no more' but in
thankfulness that he was.
—Hebrew Proverb

Blessed are those who mourn, for they
shall be comforted.
—Matthew 5:4

Give sorrow words; grief that does not speak knits up the o'er wrought heart and bids it break.

—William Shakespeare

Be content to progress in slow steps
until you have legs to run and wings
with which to fly.

—Padre Pio

No one ever told me that grief felt so much like fear.
—C.S. Lewis

There is a sacredness in tears. They are not the mark of weakness, but of power. They speak more eloquently than ten thousand tongues. They are the messengers of overwhelming grief, of deep contrition, and of unspeakable love.

—Washington Irving

I just had a broken heart. He didn't break my heart, his departure did. Now I was starting to feel his love healing my wounds.

—Grace Liang, *Finding Grace*

Darkness comes. In the middle of it, the future looks blank.
The temptation to quit is huge. Don't. You are in good company...
You will argue with yourself that there is no way forward. But with God,
nothing is impossible. He has more ropes and ladders and tunnels out
of pits than you can conceive. Wait. Pray without ceasing. Hope.

—John Piper

Hope begins in the dark, the stubborn hope that
if you just show up and try to do the right thing,
the dawn will come. You wait and watch and work:
you don't give up.
—Anne Lamott

How long will you grieve? How long will they be dead?
—David Kessler

What saves a man is to take a step.
Then another step.
—Antoine de Saint-Exupéry

People bring us well-meant but miserable consolations when they tell us what time will do to help our grief. We do not want to lose our grief, because our grief is bound up with our love and we could not cease to mourn without being robbed of our affections.

—Phillips Brooks

Grief is like the ocean; it comes in waves, ebbing and flowing. Sometimes the water is calm and sometimes it is overwhelming. All we can do is learn to swim.

—Vicki Harrison

For everything there is a season...a time to break
down, and a time to build up; a time to weep, and a
time to laugh; a time to mourn, and a time to dance...
—Ecclesiastes 3:1-4

There are no goodbyes for us.
Wherever you are, you will always be in my heart.
—Mahatma Gandhi

May you take comfort in knowing there is one
more angel above us.
—Unknown

Chapter 3:
Overcoming Obstacles

You are learning to navigate all "the firsts." They can be so challenging. Some days you feel like you are moving forward and then it's two steps backwards. It can be frustrating. Some days you see glimpses of real hope.

As you begin this chapter, consider these prompts to help you navigate your emotions as you reflect and journal.

🍃 *When I have a setback, what can I do to help myself to navigate it better next time?*

🍃 *My support system includes...*

🍃 *A simple activity or non-activity I could try today to make things easier is...*

🍃 *What can I do at this moment to make today better?*

🍃 *I celebrate my good days by...*

The following pages are filled with quotes to help prompt you to explore and capture other thoughts you might be having.

Not everything that's faced can be changed, but nothing can be changed that is not faced.
—James Baldwin

What lies behind us and what lies before us are
tiny matters compared to what lies within us.

—Ralph Waldo Emerson

The mind is everything.
What you think, you become.
—Buddha

Keep your face always toward the sunshine—
and shadows will fall behind you.
—Walt Whitman

Hardships often prepare ordinary
people for an extraordinary destiny.
—C.S. Lewis

We must accept finite disappointment,
but never lose infinite hope.
—Martin Luther King, Jr.

Whether you think you can
or you think you can't, you're right.
—Henry Ford

Everything you want is on
the other side of fear.
—Jack Canfield

I am not fully healed, I am not fully wise, I am still on my way.
What matters is that I am moving forward.
—Yung Pueblo

When everything seems to be going against you,
remember that the airplane takes off
against the wind, not with it.

—Henry Ford

Everything that happens to you is your teacher. The secret is to learn to sit at the feet of your own life and be taught by it.
—Polly B. Berends

Never bend your head. Hold it high. Look the world straight in the eye.

—Helen Keller

Try again. Fail again. Fail better.
—Samuel Beckett

Don't be ashamed to weep; 'tis right to grieve. Tears are only water, and
flowers, trees, and fruit cannot grow without water. But there must be
sunlight also. A wounded heart will heal in time, and when it does, the
memory and love of our lost ones is sealed inside to comfort us.

—Brian Jacques

Recovery is not a process we can will, but consists of experiencing many small deaths, the passing of significant anniversaries, until our identity is solid and natural in the pronoun "I."
—Mary Jane Moffat

He can, who believes he can.
—Miquel de Cervantes

I'll go anywhere as long as it's forward.
—David Livingston

I cannot change the direction of the wind,
but I can adjust my sails to always reach my destination.

—Jimmy Dean

Storms make trees take deeper roots.
—Dolly Parton

The present moment is filled with joy and happiness.
If you are attentive, you will see it.
—Thich Naht Hahn

Chapter 4:
Faith

It's in our darkest moments when leaning into our faith and spirituality that
we often find great strength. Through the power of surrender and prayer,
we trust that we do not always understand that there is a greater plan unfolding.

**As you begin this chapter, consider these prompts to help you
navigate your emotions as you reflect and journal.**

- *What prayers have I found a source of comfort during this
  season of my life?*

- *What one action can I take today that will help me to
  strengthen my faith?*

- *When I spend time in nature, I feel...*

- *How do I feel when I know others are praying for me during
  my season of grief? Who can I ask to pray for me today?*

- *How has grace touched me recently?*

The following pages are filled with quotes to help prompt you to explore
and capture other thoughts you might be having.

The very least you can do in your life is to figure out what to hope for.
And the most you can do is live inside that hope.
—Barbara Kingsolver

The Lord is near to those who have a broken
heart, and saves such as have a contrite spirit.
—Psalm 34:18

Come to Me, all who are weary and heavy-laden,
and I will give you rest.
—Matthew 11:28

God is our refuge and strength,
a very present help in trouble.
—Psalm 46:1

Fear not, for I am with you; be not dismayed, for I am your God; I will strengthen you, I will help you, I will uphold you with my righteous right hand.

—Isaiah 41:10

Have courage for the great sorrows of life and patience for the small ones; and when you have laboriously accomplished your daily task, go to sleep in peace. God is awake.

—Victor Hugo

Keep sowing your seeds for you never know which one will grow—perhaps they all will.
—The Bible

A single sunbeam is enough to drive
away many shadows.
—St. Francis of Assisi

The fishermen know that the sea is dangerous and the storm terrible, but they have never found these dangers sufficient reason for remaining ashore.
—Vincent van Gogh

Death is nothing else but going home to God,
the bond of love will be unbroken for all eternity.

—Mother Teresa

It's the nature of grace always to fill the spaces that have been empty.
—Goethe

Hope is being able to see that there is light despite all of the darkness.
—Desmond Tutu

First do what is necessary, then do what is possible, and before long you will find yourself doing the impossible.
—St. Francis of Assisi

Faith
is the bird
that feels the light
And sings
when the dawn
is still dark.
—Rabindranath Tagor

Blessed are those who mourn for
they shall be comforted.
—Matthew 5:4

There are no mistakes, no coincidences.
All events are blessings given to us to learn from.
—Elisabeth Kübler-Ross

We are what we believe we are!
—C.S. Lewis

God gave us memory
so that we might have
roses in December.
—J.M. Barrie

Everything is possible for the one who believes.
—Jesus of Nazareth

Perhaps they are not the stars, but rather openings in
Heaven where the love of our lost ones pours through and
shines down upon us to let us know that they are happy.
—Unknown

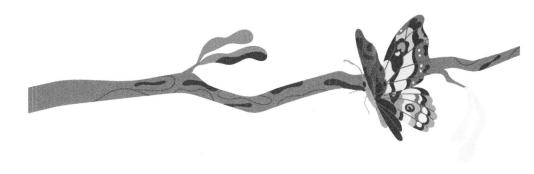

Chapter 5:
With Wisdom

The numbness is subsiding. You may be beginning to experience days that are a bit brighter. Your heart is still heavy as you try to understand the enormity of the loss of your partner and how you will navigate your path forward. You are learning how to embrace self-compassion as you uncover your own innate wisdom.

As you begin this chapter, consider these prompts to help you navigate your emotions as you reflect and journal.

- *I am ready to feel...*

- *One new thing I could try to learn or accomplish this week is...*

- *I could use a little less...*

- *To allow these feelings room to transform into something else, I am willing to...*

- *What have I learned about myself recently that has surprised me?*

The following pages are filled with quotes to help prompt you to explore and capture other thoughts you might be having.

New beginnings are often disguised as painful endings.

—Lao Tzu

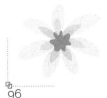

Always do what you are afraid to do.
—Ralph Waldo Emerson

Courage is only the accumulation of small steps.
—George Konrad

Do not think of me as gone.
I am with you still in each new dawn.
—Native American Poem

Those things that hurt instruct.
—Benjamin Franklin

Earth hath no sorrow that Heaven cannot heal
—Thomas Moore

We don't receive wisdom; we must discover it for
ourselves after a journey that no one can take for us
or spare us.
—Marcel Proust

Great things are not done by impulse but by
a series of small things brought together.
—Vincent van Gogh

I have just three things to teach: simplicity, patience, compassion. These are your greatest treasures. Compassionate toward yourself, you reconcile all beings in the world.
—LaoTzu

Life is not a matter of holding good cards,
but sometimes, playing a poor hand well.
—Jack London

You must do the things
you think you cannot do.
—Eleanor Roosevelt

Being able to persist is not the most important thing—
the ability to start over is.
—F. Scott Fitzgerald

Life is eternal, love is immortal, and death is only a horizon;
And a horizon is nothing save the limit of our sight.
—Rossiter Worthington Raymond

Wisdom ceases to be wisdom when it becomes too proud to weep, too
grave to laugh, and too selfish to seek other than itself.
—Kahlil Gibran

They can conquer who believe they can.
—John Dylan

Believe you can and you're halfway there.
—Theodore Roosevelt

An awake heart is like a sky that pours light.
—Hafiz

When it is darkest,
we can see the stars.
—Ralph Waldo Emerson

Hope is the thing with feathers that perches in the soul and sings the tune without the words and never stops at all.
—Emily Dickinson

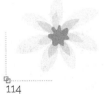

Our human compassion binds us the one to the
other – not in pity or patronizingly, but as human
beings who have learnt how to turn our common
suffering into hope for the future."
—Nelson Mandela

Chapter 6:
On Love

Your emotions are changing every day from anger and despair to uncertainty and confusion. However, the unwavering truth is that love never dies. Learning to live with your memories and the love that you still have in your heart will help you rise up, continue living and love yourself.

As you begin this chapter, consider these prompts to help you navigate your emotions as you reflect and journal.

- *Who can I connect with to share stories about my partner?*

- *What I loved most about my partner is...*

- *The memories I most treasure of the years spent together...*

- *I can honor my loved one by...*

- *What act of self-compassion and self-love can I do for myself this week?*

The following pages are filled with quotes to help prompt you to explore and capture other thoughts you might be having.

Tears shed for another person are not a sign of weakness.
They are a sign of a pure heart.
—José N. Harris

If there ever comes a day when
we can't be together, keep me in
your heart, I'll stay there forever.
—Winnie the Pooh

Unable are the loved to die. For love is immortality.

—Emily Dickinson

Death leaves a heartache no one can heal,
love leaves a memory no one can steal.
—Unknown

When we lose someone we love, we must
learn not to live without them, but to live with
the love they left behind.
—Anonymous

This is not goodbye, my darling, this is a thank you.
Thank you for coming into my life and giving me joy.
—Nicholas Sparks

To live in hearts we leave behind is not to die.
—Thomas Campbell

Only people who are capable of loving strongly can also
suffer great sorrow, but this same necessity of loving serves
to counteract their grief and heals them.

—Leo Tolstoy

Every moment of light and dark are a miracle.
—Walt Whitman

When you are sorrowful look again in your heart, and you shall see
that in truth you are weeping for that which has been your delight.

—Kahlil Gibran

When a person is born we rejoice, and when they're married we jubilate, and when they die we try to pretend nothing has happened.
—Margaret Mead

Good men must die, but death cannot kill their names.
—Proverb

Love without hope will not survive, love without faith changes nothing. Love gives power to hope and faith.
—Toba Beta

They say love beyond the world cannot be separated by it.
Death cannot kill what never dies.

—William Penn

The risk of love is loss, and the price of loss is grief –
But the pain of grief is only a shadow when compared
with the pain of never risking love.
—Hilary Stanton Zunin

Don't let the fear of striking out hold you back.
—Babe Ruth

What is lovely never dies, but passes into other loveliness.
—Thomas Bailey

To have been loved so deeply, even though the person
who loved us is gone, will give us some protection forever.

—J.K. Rowling

Those we love don't go away,
they walk beside us every day...unseen, unheard,
but always near, still loved, still missed, and very dear.
—Unknown

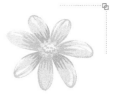

What is lovely never dies, but passes into another loveliness,
Star-dust or sea-foam,
Flower or winged air.
—Thomas Bailey Aldrich

Chapter 7:
On Gratitude

As time passes, you start to see all the blessings that have been surrounding you all along. Through your sadness, you are still able to be thankful for the kindness others have extended to you. May you experience gratitude with wonder and delight.

As you begin this chapter, consider these prompts to help you navigate your emotions as you reflect and journal.

- *I accomplished today and I feel...*

- *Who can I reach out to today and tell them why I am grateful for them in my life?*

- *Five things I am grateful for today...*

- *What activities can I do to help me be more heart-centered?*

- *Who can I be of service to today?*

The following pages are filled with quotes to help prompt you to explore and capture other thoughts you might be having.

But listen to me. For one moment quit being sad.
Hear blessings dropping their blossoms around you.
—Rumi

Someone I loved once gave me a box full of darkness.
It took me years to understand that this, too, was a gift.

—Mary Oliver

We should feel sorrow, but not sink under its oppression.
—Confucius

Gratitude is when memory is stored
in the heart and not in the mind.
—Lionel Hampton

I still miss those I loved who are no longer with me
but I find I am grateful for having loved them.
The gratitude has finally conquered the loss.
—Rita Mae Brown

Give thanks for what you are today and go on fighting for
what you're going to be tomorrow.
—William Shakespeare

Gratitude consists of being more aware of what you have, than what you don't.
—Unknown

Remember the past with gratitude. Live the present with
enthusiasm. Look forward to the future with confidence.
—St. John Paul II

If you say only one prayer in a day,
make it thank you.
—Rumi

In the midst of winter, I discovered that there was
in me an invincible summer.

—Albert Camus

When you recognize that you will thrive not in spite of your losses and sorrows but because of them...the word for that is healing.
—Cheryl Strayed

Wear gratitude like a cloak, and it will feed every
corner of your life.

—Rumi

Give thanks for the little and you will find a lot.
—Hausa proverb from Nigeria

Gratitude for the present moment and the
fullness of life now is the true prosperity.
—Eckhart Tolle

Those who bring sunshine to their lives of others cannot keep it from themselves.
—J.M. Barrie

The best way to show my gratitude to God is to accept
everything, even my problems, with joy.
—St. Teresa of Calcutta

Decide what you want. Believe you can have it. Believe you deserve it and believe it's possible for you. And then close your eyes and every day for several minutes, and visualize having what you already want, feeling the feelings of already having it. Come out of that and focus on what you're grateful for already, and really enjoy it. Then go into your day and release it to the Universe and trust that the Universe will figure out how to manifest it.

—Jack Canfield

May you be safe.
May you be happy.
May you be healthy.
May you live with ease.
—Metta prayer

Your success and happiness lie in you...
Resolve to keep happy, and your joy and
you shall form an invincible host against difficulties.
—Helen Keller

Like a bird singing in the rain, let grateful memories
survive in time of sorrow.
—Robert Louis Stevenson

Chapter 8:
On Money

Money has a way of stirring up emotions. As you navigate your financial life going forward, you want to make sure you are doing so from a place of knowledge, rather than fear or ignorance. It's your money and your life— be in charge!

As you begin this chapter, consider these prompts to help you navigate your emotions as you reflect and journal.

- *What I fear or don't understand about my finances is...*

- *What would I like my financial life to look like in five years?*

- *One thing I can do today to improve my financial life is...*

- *I feel most empowered about my finances when...*

- *If I were to ask for help or guidance about money, what would I ask for?*

The following pages are filled with quotes to help prompt you to explore and capture other thoughts you might be having.

Prince Charmings leave,
Prince Charmings die,
Prince Charmings aren't always
such great money managers.
Your job is to participate in
financial decisions from a
place of knowledge, not fear, ignorance or habit.
—Barbara Stanny

The stock market is filled with individuals who know the price of everything, but the value of nothing.
—Phillip Fisher

An investment in knowledge pays the best interest.
—Benjamin Franklin

You must gain control over your money
or the lack of it will forever control you.
—Dave Ramsey

Wealth consists not in having great possessions,
but in having few wants.
—Epictetus

Never spend your money before you have it.

—Thomas Jefferson

Money is a good servant but a bad master.
—Francis Bacon, Sr.

Buy when everyone else is selling
and hold until everyone else is buying.
That's not just a catchy slogan. It's the very essence
of successful investing.
—J. Paul Getty

A good financial plan is a road map that shows us exactly how the choices we make today will affect our future.
—Alexa Von Tobel

Money is only a tool. It will take you wherever you wish,
but it will not replace you as the driver.

—Ayn Rand

It's good to have money and the things that money can buy, but it's good, too, to check up once in a while and make sure that you haven't lost the things that money can't buy.
—George Horace Lorimer

Beware of little expenses.
A small leak will sink a great ship.
—Benjamin Franklin

Only buy something that you'd be perfectly happy to hold if the market shuts down for ten years.

—Warren Buffett

Know what you own, and know why you own it.

—Peter Lynch

Don't tell me where your priorities are. Show me where you spend your money and I'll tell you what they are.
—James W. Frick

What we really want to do is what we are really meant to do. When we do what we are meant to do, money comes to us, doors open for us, we feel useful, and the work we do feels like play to us.

—Julia Cameron

A big part of financial freedom is having your heart and mind free from worry about the what-ifs of life.
—Suze Orman

It's not how much money you make, but how much money you keep, how hard it works for you, and how many generations you keep it for.

—Robert Kiyosaki

Wealth is the ability to fully experience life.
—Henry David Thoreau

You can only become truly accomplished at something you love. Don't make money your goal. Instead, pursue the things you love doing, and then do them so well that people can't take their eyes off you.

—Maya Angelou

Chapter 9:
Moving Forward On My Own

The fog has lifted. Your good days outnumber the days filled with unbearable sadness. You are believing in yourself and what you are capable of accomplishing. Your journey continues step by step. You are ready to move forward.

As you begin this chapter, consider these prompts to help you navigate your emotions as you reflect and journal.

- *Today I will honor myself by accomplishing...*

- *Who can I reach out to today to tell them why I am grateful for them in my life?*

- *When I am overcome by grief, here is a mantra or affirmation I can use to comfort and encourage myself...*

- *What new commitment will I make for myself?*

- *How far have I come and grown? As I reflect, I will give myself credit for...*

The following pages are filled with quotes to help prompt you to explore and capture other thoughts you might be having.

When one door is shut, another opens.

—Miquel de Cervantes

Life isn't about waiting for the storm to pass...
it's about learning to dance in the rain.
—Vivian Greene

You cannot swim for new horizons until you have courage
to lose sight of the shore.
—William Faulkner

You can't fall if you don't climb. But there is no
joy in living your whole life on the ground.
—Unknown

There is something you must always remember.
You are braver than you believe, stronger than
you seem, and smarter than you think.
—Winnie the Pooh

A journey of a thousand miles begins with a single step.

—Lao Tzu

She took a step and she didn't want to take any more, but she did.
—Markus Zusak, *The Book Thief*

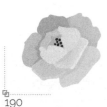

If you have the courage to begin,
you have the courage to succeed.
—David Viscott

Nothing ever goes away until it has taught us
what we need to know.
—Pema Chodron

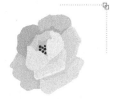

People say, 'What is the sense of our small efforts?'
They cannot see that we must lay one brick at a time,
take one step at a time.
—Dorothy Day

Hope can be a powerful force. Maybe there's no actual magic in it, but when you know what you hope for most and hold it like a light within you, you can make things happen, almost like magic.

—Laini Taylor

It's your life. The one you must make in the obliterated place that is now your world, where everything you used to be is simultaneously erased and omnipresent. The obliterated place is equal parts destruction and creation. The obliterated place is pitch black and bright light. It is water and parched earth. It is mud and it is manna. The real work of deep grief is making a home there.

—Cheryl Strayed, *Tiny Little Things*

First you jump off the cliff and then
you build your wings on the way down.
　—Ray Bradbury

The greatest glory in living lies not in never falling,
but in rising every time we fall.
—Nelson Mandela

We can't control our destiny,
but we can control who we become.
—Anne Frank

Believe in yourself and all that you are. Know that there is something inside you that is greater than any obstacle.
—Christina D. Larson

A ship is safe in harbor, but that's not what ships are for.
—William G.T. Shedd

Every widow wakes one morning, perhaps after years
of pure and unwavering grieving, to realize she slept
a good night's sleep, and will be able to eat breakfast,
and doesn't hear her husband's ghost all the time, but
only some of the time. Her grief is replaced with a useful
sadness...we learn to live in that love.
—Jonathan Safran Foer, *Everything Is Illuminated*

They seemed to come suddenly upon happiness as if
they had surprised a butterfly in the winter woods.
—Edith Wharton

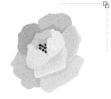

Hope smiles from the threshold of the year to come,
whispering 'it will be happier'...
—Alfred Lord Tennyson

Chapter 10:
Living Again

You acknowledge that you will still grieve and love your partner. One of the best ways to do that is by fully living your life again. You are ready to rediscover yourself and who you are right now. You are digging deep to write this next chapter of your life's journey.

As you begin this chapter, consider these prompts to help you navigate your emotions as you reflect and journal.

- *What does "living" mean to me right now?*

- *The new picture of my life looks like...*

- *What I need to feel whole again at this point in my life is...*

- *I feel confident when I am...*

- *What one word can I use as a mantra as I move forward?*

The following pages are filled with quotes to help prompt you to explore and capture other thoughts you might be having.

Sometimes you have to let go of the picture of what you thought life would be like and learn to find joy in the story you are actually living.
—Rachel Marie Martin

And so I wait. I wait for time to heal the pain and raise me
to my feet once again - so that I can start a new path, my
own path, the one that will make me whole again.

—Jack Canfield

When one door of happiness closes, another opens, but we look so long at the closed door that we do not see the one that has been opened for us.
—Helen Keller

Let your hopes, not your hurts,
shape your future.
—Robert H. Schuller

You may be disappointed if you fail,
but you are doomed if you don't try.
—Beverly Sills

Taking the first step, uttering a new word
is what people fear most.
—Fyodor Dostoyevsky

The best way to find yourself is to
lose yourself in the service of others.
—Mahatma Gandhi

Action may not always bring happiness, but
there is no happiness without action.
—Benjamin Disraeli

The man who moves a mountain begins
by carrying away small stones.
—Confucius

The real voyage of discovery consists not in seeking
new landscapes but in having new eyes.
—Miquel Proust

Never get tired of doing little things for others.
Sometimes those little things occupy the biggest
part of their hearts.
—St. Therese of Lisieux

With the new day comes new strength and new thoughts.

—Eleanor Roosevelt

"Come to the edge," he said.
They said, "We are afraid."
"Come to the edge," he said again.
They came.
He pushed them...and they flew.
—Guillaume Apollinaire

Nothing is impossible,
the word itself says, "I'm possible."
—Audrey Hepburn

I'm choosing happiness over suffering, I know I am.
I'm making space for the unknown future to fill up
my life with yet-to-come surprises.
—**Elizabeth Gilbert,** *Eat, Love, Pray*

Swim with the tide.
—Anonymous

Leap and the net will appear.
—John Burroughs

The purpose of human life is to serve, and to show
compassion and the will to help others.
—Albert Schweitzer

You gain strength, courage, and confidence by every experience in which you really stop to look fear in the face. You are able to say to yourself. "I lived through this horror. I can take the next thing that comes along." We must do the things we think we cannot.
—Eleanor Roosevelt

Hope is the only bee that makes honey without flowers.
—Robert Green Ingersoll

Here's why I invited you on this healing journey.

My grandmother Mary was widowed at 50. She never remarried.

So much of what I learned from her is what I bring forward into my financial planning practice at WH Cornerstone Investments. That's where we get to help one widow at a time get back on her feet, rise up, and navigate her path forward.

As a widow, Mary devoted the next 25 years of her life to serving others, especially reaching out to the senior citizens in her community. She understood that she could empower others with what life had taught her.

My mission is to empower women to make decisions from a place of knowledge – and not of fear – and to be prepared for any unexpected curve balls in life.

My prayer for you is that this journal has helped you gain insight and healing along your journey.

May the time invested here gift you with the strength, courage, hope and conviction to embrace the full life that awaits you.

About the author

Paula Harris is part financial advisor and part dream architect, who takes great pride in helping her clients, particularly widowed women, obtain financial peace of mind while they get back on their feet and navigate forward.

Paula is an engaging speaker, author, and leader. She enjoys assisting women in the life planning that goes hand-in-hand with financial planning and is the creator of Rise Up Success Training and Retreats as well as Wisdom Wednesday which can be found on her YouTube channel where she shares her positivity, pondering and prayers.

She can be reached at **www.whcornerstone.com.**

Made in the USA
Coppell, TX
10 January 2022

71370948R00134